Rise and Shine, Andy Capp!

Smythe

A FAWCETT GOLD MEDAL BOOK

Fawcett Publications, Inc., Greenwich, Connecticut

RISE AND SHINE, ANDY CAPP!

ANDY CAPP of the Daily Mirror, London

Published by special arrangement with Field Newspaper Syndicate

Printed in the United States of America

First printing: July 1975

1 2 3 4 5 6 7 8 9 10

11-13-72

11-23-72

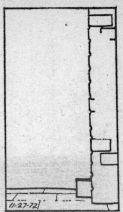

11-27-72

ANDY! ME BOSS'S LOWERED ME RETIRIN' AGE T' SIXTY! ON HALF PAY, TOO—!

11-29-72

WHAT D'YER THINK OF EMPLOYERS *NOW*, PET?

I'LL *TELL* YER! CAST YER MIND BACK TWENTY YEARS — DID 'E OR DID 'E NOT SWEAR TO ME YER JOB WAS *PERMANENT*?!

Smythe

12-8-72

FUNNY, 'OW THINGS WORK OUT —

12-16-72

— WHEN I WAS YOUNG I 'AD AN AMBITION TO TRAVEL

BONK

12-25-72

12-28-72

1-13-73

NICE BUMPIN' INTO YOU, PET, BUT I GUESS Y' LUNCH HOUR'S UP AN' I KNOW YOU LIKE TO BE GAINFULLY EMPLOYED

2-5-73

AN' YOU'D BETTER RUN OFF 'OME, IT LOOKS LIKE RAIN

ARMS

BINGO

WE 'AVE THIS PROPER BASIS FOR MARRIAGE — MUTUAL MISUNDERSTANDIN'

Smythe

2-9-73

BY THE WAY THERE'S A CUP MATCH DOWN SOUTH ON SATURDAY, AN' I'LL BE STAYIN' OVERNIGHT. IT MEANS LEAVIN' YER ON YER OWN — WILL YER BE ALL RIGHT?

2-15-73

Smythe

I'LL MANAGE

2-16-73

CLICK

THERE'S NOTHIN' SO CONSOLIN' AS FINDIN' THAT YOUR NEIGHBOUR'S TROUBLES ARE AT LEAST AS BIG AS YOUR OWN

2-24-73

Smythe

3-12-73

3-27-73

4-10-73

IT'S BOUND TO GET AROUND...

EVEN THE POOR PEOPLE 'AVE THEIR POOR RELATIONS

Smythe

Fawcett Gold Medal Books
in the Andy Capp Series
by Smythe

ANDY CAPP, MAN OF THE HOUR	T3072	75¢
ANDY CAPP SOUNDS OFF	T3079	75¢
ANDY CAPP STRIKES BACK *(abridged)*	T3080	75¢
ANDY CAPP, THE ONE AND ONLY	T3081	75¢
HATS OFF TO ANDY CAPP	T3102	75¢
HURRAY FOR ANDY CAPP *(abridged)*	T3036	75¢
IN YOUR EYE, ANDY CAPP *(abridged)*	T3107	75¢
IT'S PUB TIME, ANDY CAPP	M3243	95¢
LIVE IT UP, ANDY CAPP	T2965	75¢
MEET ANDY CAPP	T3112	75¢
NONE OF YOUR LIP, ANDY CAPP!	T3174	75¢
RISE AND SHINE, ANDY CAPP!	M3258	95¢
TAKE A BOW, ANDY CAPP	T3133	75¢
THE UNDISPUTED ANDY CAPP	T3119	75¢
VERY SNEAKY, ANDY CAPP	T3120	75¢
WATCH YOUR STEP, ANDY CAPP	T3123	75¢
WHAT NEXT, ANDY CAPP	T3124	75¢
YOU'RE A RIOT, ANDY CAPP	T3128	75¢
YOU'RE SOME HERO, ANDY CAPP	T3129	75¢
YOU TELL 'EM, ANDY CAPP	T3131	75¢
YOU'RE THE BOSS, ANDY CAPP	T3130	75¢

FAWCETT

Wherever Paperbacks Are Sold

If your bookdealer is sold out, send cover price plus 35¢ each for postage and handling to Mail Order Department, Fawcett Publications, Inc., P.O. Box 1014, Greenwich, Connecticut 06830. Please order by number and title. Catalog available on request.